# The Stone Stew

Written by Rozanne Lanczak Williams
Created by Sue Lewis
Illustrated by Patty Briles

*Creative Teaching Press*

**The Story of Stone Stew**
© 2002 Creative Teaching Press, Inc.
Written by Rozanne Lanczak Williams
Illustrated by Patty Briles
Project Manager: Sue Lewis
Project Director: Carolea Williams

Published in the United States of America by:
Creative Teaching Press, Inc.
P.O. Box 2723
Huntington Beach, CA  92647-0723

All rights reserved. No part of this book may be reproduced in any form without the written permission of Creative Teaching Press, Inc.

CTP 3246

You start with some stones.

You stir them around.

You add in some sticks. . .

that you found
on the ground.

Stir in more stuff.

It's stupendous stone stew!

M-m-m-m! Yummy, yummy!

It's stone stew for you!

# Create your own book!

Write your own story about how to make stone stew. Attach a resealable plastic bag to the cover of your book. Store your ingredients in the bag (stones, sticks, plastic bugs, pictures, etc.). Attach a plastic bag to each of the inside pages. As you read the book, place the matching ingredients inside the pockets.

# Words in *The Story of Stone Stew*

| Blends: *st* | High-Frequency Words | Other |
|---|---|---|
| story | the | some |
| stone | you | around |
| stones | with | found |
| stew | them | ground |
| start | that | add |
| stir | in | more |
| sticks | on | m-m-m-m |
| stuff | for | yummy |
| stupendous | of | it's |